Look! Listen! Think!

Grades 6-7

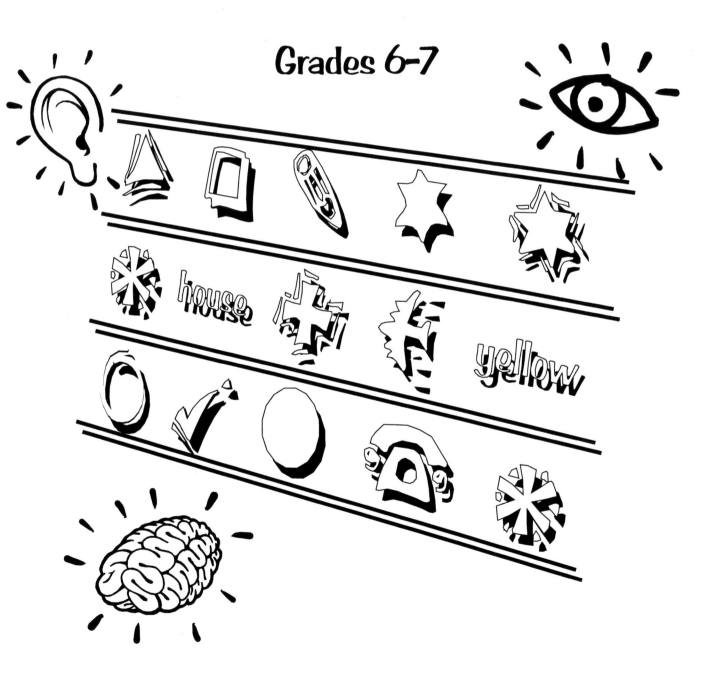

Written by Jean Edwards

Published by World Teachers Press®

Mrs. Cole
O.T.

Order Number 2-5096
ISBN 978-1-58324-018-2

B C D E F 11 10 09 08 07

395 Main Street
Rowley, MA 01969
www.didax.com

Foreword ◀‖‖

Look! Listen! Think! is a series of three books designed to provide you with activities to exercise the minds of your students.

Each book contains a series of developmental activities in the following areas:

(i)   Visual discrimination and memory skills—being able to remember what they have seen and answer questions accordingly; and

(ii) Listening comprehension and memory skills—being able to remember what they have heard and follow oral instructions correctly.

Both sections provide you with detailed information to ensure the procedures are easy to follow and administer. Sections can be tackled in any order, but the activities within each section gradually become more difficult, so should be used from set one through to the final set.

Contents ◀‖‖

Teacher Information...

...Visual Memory Skills ◀▥▥

- Distribute the picture to students. It may be cut off separately or the question side may be folded back.

- Students study the picture for a time you specify. (Suggestion – thirty seconds for grades six and seven.)

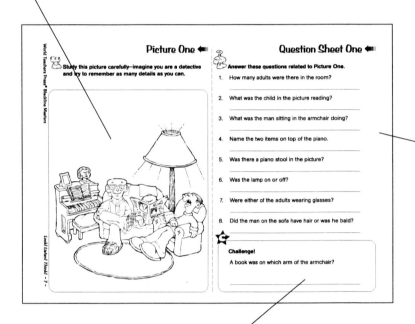

- Picture is turned over.

- Students answer questions. You may read questions if there are reading difficulties.

- Activity may also be given verbally on an individual basis with you writing the responses.

- Challenge! is answered but not recorded on scoring sheet.

- Distribute a scoring sheet from page 18 to each student.

- Scores can be recorded by:

    (a) students individually checking the picture;

    (b) teacher marking individually; or

    (c) teacher discussing answers with the whole class.

- Do not ask the students to call out their score unless they are comfortable with this approach.

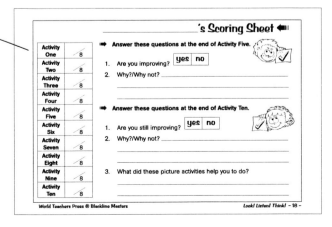

Teacher Information...

...Listening Memory Skills ◀███

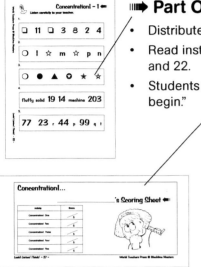

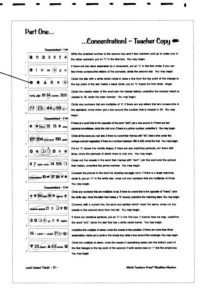

███➤ Part One – Concentration!

- Distribute student activity page.
- Read instructions from teacher copy on pages 21 and 22.
- Students complete each row after you say, "You may begin."

  - Distribute a scoring sheet from page 28 to each student.
  - Scores can be recorded by:
    (a) teacher marking individually; or
    (b) teacher discussing answers with the whole class.
  - Do not ask the students to call out their score unless they are comfortable with this approach.

███➤ Part Two – Item Missing

- Distribute a scoring sheet from page 32 to each student.

- Administer "Item Missing" activities to students from pages 30 and 31.

- Student writes missing item on scoring sheet.
- Supply the answers and students record their score.
- Do not ask students to call out their score unless they are comfortable with this approach.

███➤ Parts Three and Four – Digits Forwards and Digits Backwards

- Distribute a scoring sheet from page 36 or 40 to each student.
- Administer the "Digits Forwards" activities from pages 34 and 35, and "Digits Backwards" activities from pages 38 and 39.
- Student writes the sequence of digits on the scoring sheet whether it be forwards or backwards.

- Supply the answers and students record their score.
- Do not ask students to call out their score unless they are comfortable with this approach.
- Challenge! is answered on the sheet but not recorded in the total.

Visual Memory Skills

Visual discrimination and visual memory skills form an integral part of many daily activities. They are essential and critical skill areas, but we don't often, or regularly teach, or consciously develop them in our classroom program.

Visual discrimination and visual memory skills can be enhanced by practice and your students will benefit from regular exercises at least once a week. These activities will help to provide that practice.

You can explain to your students that the mind is rather like a muscle, in that it can be exercised and strengthened and that these activities are designed to provide that exercise.

The illustrations on the following pages are to help improve visual discrimination and visual memory skills. The activities become gradually more difficult.

The pages have been designed to be used in two ways.

1. You can cut the page down the middle and distribute the picture. The students turn the illustration over after studying it and you read the questions.

2. The students fold the page down the middle and study the picture side. Then they turn it over to answer the questions without being able to see the picture. Be sure students do not read the questions before studying the picture.

In this section students are required to remember what they have seen in the picture and answer questions accordingly.

Instructions

➠ Tell the students that the activity is to help them with their visual memory—remembering details of what they have seen. (Like playing detective.)

➠ Distribute a copy of the illustration to each student and allow them a stated time to scan the illustration; for example, thirty seconds for students in grades six and seven.

➠ Turn the illustration over and answer the questions on the answer sheet—this allows students to work at their own pace.

➠ You can also read the questions, allowing suitable time for answering if there are reading difficulties.

➠ The activity can also be given verbally on an individual basis, with you writing down the student's responses.

Scoring

➠ Students can mark their own work, by checking the illustration, or you can discuss the answers with the students.

➠ Students enter their score on the scoring sheet provided on page 18.

Question Sheet One

Answer these questions related to Picture One.

1. How many adults were there in the room?

2. What was the child in the picture reading?

3. What was the man sitting in the armchair doing?

4. Name the two items on top of the piano.

5. Was there a piano stool in the picture?

6. Was the lamp on or off?

7. Were either of the adults wearing glasses?

8. Did the man on the sofa have hair or was he bald?

Challenge!

A book was on which arm of the armchair?

Picture One

Study this picture carefully—imagine you are a detective and try to remember as many details as you can.

Question Sheet Two

Answer these questions related to Picture Two.

1. How many people were sitting on the park bench?

2. How many people were on the swings?

3. How many people were on the slide?

4. Where was the rubbish bin in this picture?

5. Was either of the women on the bench wearing glasses?

6. Did the elderly man have a scarf on?

7. What pattern was on the elderly man's trousers?

8. What was the dangerous situation in the picture?

Challenge!

Was the person on the swings on the left or the right swing as seen from our point of view?

Picture Two

Study this picture carefully–imagine you are a detective and try to remember as many details as you can.

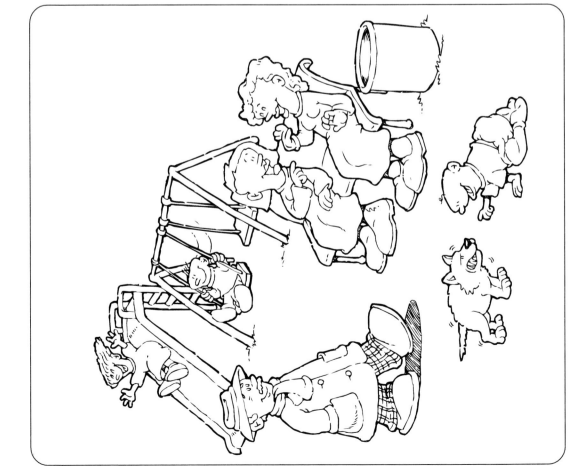

Question Sheet Three

Answer these questions related to Picture Three.

1. Name the two streets in this picture.

2. Which way was the motorcyclist signaling he wanted to turn?

3. What item was lying on the road?

4. What was the make of the truck waiting at the crossroads?

5. Who was pushing the baby's carriage—mother or father?

6. What did the baby in the carriage have in its hand?

7. Who was driving the car—a man or a woman?

8. How many people could you see sitting in the truck?

Challenge!

How many streetlights were visible?

Picture Three

Study this picture carefully—imagine you are a detective and try to remember as many details as you can.

HIGH ST.

TUFF

EDWARDS ST.

SCENIC ROUTE

GIVE WAY

MQ 5656

Question Sheet Four

Answer these questions related to Picture Four.

1. How many students were in their seats?

2. How many student desks were there altogether?

3. Was it a girl or a boy painting with their back to us?

4. What was the time on the clock?

5. What was the wall poster underneath the clock about?

6. Did the classroom door have a glass panel in it?

7. Did the teacher have dark or light hair?

8. What was the correct answer for the sum on the board?

Challenge!

Assuming there was one desk for each student, how many students were absent or out of the classroom?

Picture Four

Study this picture carefully—imagine you are a detective and try to remember as many details as you can.

Question Sheet Five

Answer these questions related to Picture Five.

1. What was the man in the suit holding in his left hand?

    _____

2. What design was on his tie?

    _____

3. Is the woman smiling at the person on her left or her right?

    _____

4. How many buttons could you see on the bearded man's waistcoat?

    _____

5. Did the woman have buttons or a zipper on her jogging suit?

    _____

6. What is the bearded man holding in his left hand?

    _____

7. Did the woman have laces on her shoes?

    _____

8. Was there an antenna visible on the mobile phone?

    _____

☆ Challenge!
Which person was out of step with the other two?

_____

Picture Five

Study this picture carefully–imagine you are a detective and try to remember as many details as you can.

Question Sheet Six

Answer these questions related to Picture Six.

1. How many people were standing just inside the entrance?

2. What did the sign outside the park entrance say?

3. What words were printed on the back of the vehicle?

4. Did the vehicle have a roof-rack?

5. Which way were the rest rooms—to our left or right?

6. Which way was the Petting Zoo as you enter?

7. What was in the same direction as the Petting Zoo?

8. Did the man in the picture have light or dark hair?

Challenge!
What was the license plate number of the vehicle?

Picture Six

Study this picture carefully—imagine you are a detective and try to remember as many details as you can.

Question Sheet Seven

Answer these questions related to Picture Seven.

1. How many skateboards were in the picture?
    _____

2. Were there two birds in the sky?
    _____

3. What was on the helmet of the rollerblader on the half pipe?
    _____

4. Was everyone wearing shorts?
    _____

5. Was the ladder for the half pipe to our left or right?
    _____

6. Did the dog in the picture have spots?
    _____

7. What was the number on the girl's top?
    _____

8. In what hand was the boy holding the dog leash?
    _____

Challenge!

How many children were using rollerblades?
_____

Picture Seven

Study this picture carefully—imagine you are a detective and try to remember as many details as you can.

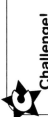

Look! Listen! Think! – 13 –

Question Sheet Eight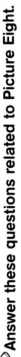

Answer these questions related to Picture Eight.

1. How many clowns were in the picture?

2. Was there an audience in the picture?

3. How many balls were being juggled by the clowns?

4. Were any clowns riding a unicycle?

5. Was there anyone wearing glasses?

6. Were there any balloons in the picture?

7. How many people were on a trapeze?

8. How many clowns were wearing hats?

 **Challenge!**

How many clowns had spots on their costume?

Picture Eight

Study this picture carefully – imagine you are a detective and try to remember as many details as you can.

Question Sheet Nine ◄▐▐▐

Answer these questions related to Picture Nine.

1. How many people were sitting at the table?

2. How many glasses were in the picture?

3. Did the table have a potted plant on it?

4. What was the boy, with his back to us, doing at the table?

5. Were the curtains open or closed?

6. What was the day and month circled on the calendar?

7. Did the cat leaning against the man have a collar?

8. Was there a fork on the counter top?

Challenge!

What was the photograph in the picture frame?

Picture Nine ◄▐▐▐

Study this picture carefully—imagine you are a detective and try to remember as many details as you can.

Question Sheet Ten

Answer these questions related to Picture Ten.

1. Who was about to step on a dropped ice cream cone?

_____

2. How many people were wearing glasses in the picture?

_____

3. Did the shoes in the store window cost $80.00?

_____

4. What was the tall boy carrying in his left hand?

_____

5. What was the shape of the lady's earrings?

_____

6. Was anyone wearing a hat?

_____

7. What was the boy by himself reading?

_____

8. Which way was the Food Court sign pointing—to our left or right? _____

Challenge!

How many buttons could you see on the lady's jacket?

_____

Picture Ten

Study this picture carefully—imagine you are a detective and try to remember as many details as you can.

Answers...

Picture One – Page 7

1. two
2. newspaper
3. sleeping
4. frame, statue
5. yes
6. on
7. yes
8. bald
☆ right

Picture Two – Page 8

1. two
2. one
3. one
4. next to park bench
5. no
6. yes
7. checks
8. child with dog
☆ left

Picture Three – Page 9

1. Edwards, High
2. right
3. can
4. TUFF
5. father
6. bunny/rabbit/toy
7. woman
8. one
☆ three

Picture Four – Page 10

1. seven
2. fifteen
3. girl
4. 3 o'clock
5. planets/space
6. yes
7. light
8. 244
☆ four

Picture Five – Page 11

1. mobile phone
2. stripes
3. left
4. six
5. zipper
6. bag
7. yes
8. yes
☆ man in suit

Picture Six – Page 12

1. two
2. please don't feed the animals
3. wildlife park
4. yes
5. left
6. right
7. train rides
8. dark
☆ QP7-496

Picture Seven – Page 13

1. two
2. no
3. star
4. no
5. left
6. yes
7. 23
8. left
☆ three

Picture Eight – Page 14

1. seven
2. yes
3. four
4. yes
5. yes
6. no
7. two
8. three
☆ one

Picture Nine – Page 15

1. three
2. four
3. no
4. feeding the dog
5. open
6. August 8
7. no
8. no
☆ grandmother/woman

Picture Ten – Page 16

1. lady with handbag
2. one
3. no
4. bag
5. triangles
6. no
7. comic book
8. right
☆ four

_____ 's Scoring Sheet ◀||||

Activity One	/8
Activity Two	/8
Activity Three	/8
Activity Four	/8
Activity Five	/8
Activity Six	/8
Activity Seven	/8
Activity Eight	/8
Activity Nine	/8
Activity Ten	/8

➡ **Answer these questions at the end of Activity Five.**

1. Are you improving? | yes | no |

2. Why?/Why not? _____

_____

_____

➡ **Answer these questions at the end of Activity Ten.**

1. Are you still improving? | yes | no |

2. Why?/Why not? _____

_____

_____

3. What did these picture activities help you to do?

_____

_____

_____ 's Scoring Sheet ◀||||

Activity One	/8
Activity Two	/8
Activity Three	/8
Activity Four	/8
Activity Five	/8
Activity Six	/8
Activity Seven	/8
Activity Eight	/8
Activity Nine	/8
Activity Ten	/8

➡ **Answer these questions at the end of Activity Five.**

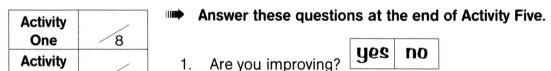

1. Are you improving? | yes | no |

2. Why?/Why not? _____

_____

_____

➡ **Answer these questions at the end of Activity Ten.**

1. Are you still improving? | yes | no |

2. Why?/Why not? _____

_____

3. What did these picture activities help you to do?

_____

_____

Listening Memory Skills

Listening and memory skills form an integral part of many daily activities, such as reading, spelling, writing and mathematics.

They are essential and critical skill areas that are not often isolated for specific development and attention in our classroom program.

Listening and memory skills can be enhanced by practice and your students will benefit from regular exercises at least once a week. These activities will help to provide that practice. They are structured to provide your students with practice in auditory memory, auditory discrimination, memory and concentration skills.

You can explain to your students that the mind is rather like a muscle, in that it can be exercised and strengthened and that these activities are designed to provide that exercise.

The activities in this section are divided into the following subsections:

➠   Concentration!—*listening, concentration and memory*

➠   Item Missing—*listening and memory*

➠   Digits Forwards—*listening and memory*

➠   Digits Backwards—*listening, concentration and memory*

The subsections may be used in any order, however, the sequences within each subsection are in ascending order of difficulty and it is recommended that you follow them through in their entirety.

Part One...

...Concentration!

In this section, students are required to listen carefully to oral instructions and complete the activity.

The *Concentration!* activities in this section gradually become more complex. Therefore, it is suggested that you work through the activities in the order they are presented. The activities are designed to develop listening, concentration and memory skills with an emphasis on concentration.

Instructions

➠ Tell the students that this activity is designed to help them practice and sharpen their concentration skills. You are going to read a sentence telling them things they can do with each row of pictures or symbols, so they need to listen carefully. You will not be repeating any of the instructions, so they need to listen and concentrate as best they can.

➠ Tell the students that you are going to do the whole page, one row at a time.

➠ Ask them not to make any noise or ask any questions once you have begun, otherwise, they might distract someone else who is trying hard to concentrate.

➠ Tell the students that you are going to read the instructions for each row of symbols. The students are to listen and refrain from working until they hear you say, "You may begin."

➠ Once you have finished giving the instructions, the students then try to remember what you have said and do their work on their activity sheet. Stress that students are not to begin working until you have said "You may begin."

   NOTE: Tell your students that if they copy the work of others here, it is only defeating themselves as they won't be training themselves to be better listeners. Being honest with themselves here sets them up for success with more difficult sets in the future.

➠ When you are ready to begin, read aloud each instruction slowly, deliberately and clearly. Give the students ample time to complete each row before moving on to the next. Use one activity sheet per session. The activity has been copied twice on the page to reduce the amount of photocopying.

Scoring

➠ Use the answers on the *Teacher Copy* (page 21 and 22) to correct the students' work. Record scores on the scoring sheet on page 28.

➠ NOTE: The scoring sheets are designed so students can monitor their own individual progress—they are not designed to compare scores with anyone else. Please avoid asking the students to call their scores aloud in front of the class unless the students say they are quite comfortable with this. You may collect totals individually instead.

Part One...

...Concentration! – Teacher Copy ◀IIII

Concentration! – 1 ◀IIII

1. ⊠ 11 ☑ 3 8 2 4

2. ⊗ l ☆ m ✪ p n

3. ⊗ ● ▲ ✪ ☆ ✪

4. fluffy solid 19 ⑭ machine 203

5. ⑦⑦ 23 (r) ⑭⑭ (p) ⑨⑨ (q) t

Concentration! – 2 ◀IIII

1. ❄ ❄ float **19** 15 ❄ plug

2. 1⑦⑦ ②⑭④ pear carrot **190** yacht

3. ✪ ☆ ▢ ○ ✪ ✪ ☆

4. 4 *7* heart circle 14 105 ○

5. elephant palm 19 ☎ *27 36* ☎ ❄

Concentration! – 3 ◀IIII

1. ★ ★ ㊱ light ⑱ ◆ squirrel ★

2. telephone general 21 ☆ ▢ ☎ 19

3. ⊠ ✪ ▢ ✪ ant ☆ ✪ dolphin

4. **16** ! rabbit ! weasel **21** ▢ ! ▢ !

5. ▼ 23 dessert ▲ ㊿ scholar ☑

Write the smallest number in the second box and if two numbers add up to make one of the other numbers, put an "x" in the first box. You may begin.

If there are two stars separated by a consonant, put an "x" in the first circle; if you can find three consecutive letters of the alphabet, circle the second star. You may begin.

Circle the star with a white circle inside it; draw a line from the top point of the triangle to the top point of the star inside a black circle; put an "x" inside the first circle. You may begin.

Circle the middle letter of the word with the fewest letters; underline the number which is closest to sixteen; circle the even number. You may begin.

Circle any numbers that are multiples of eleven; if there are any letters that are consecutive in the alphabet, circle them; put a box around the number that is closest to thirty. You may begin.

If there is a word that is the opposite of the word "sink," put a box around it; if there are two identical snowflakes, circle the odd one; if there is a prime number, underline it. You may begin.

Circle all the twos you can see; if there is a word that rhymes with "lot," draw a line under the orange-colored vegetable; if there is a number between 160 & 200, circle the fruit. You may begin.

Put an "x" above the middle shape; if there are any matching symbols, join them with lines; circle the symbols of which there is only one. You may begin.

Cross out the vowels in the word that rhymes with "dart;" join the word and the symbol that match; underline the prime number. You may begin.

Connect the phone to the hand by drawing a squiggly cord; if there is a large mammal, circle it; put an "x" in the white star; cross out any numbers that are multiples of three. You may begin.

Circle any numbers that are multiples of six; if there is a word that is the opposite of "heavy," color the white star; circle the letter that makes a "k" sound; underline the matching stars. You may begin.

Connect, with a curved line, the word and symbol which mean the same; cross out any vowels in the second word from the left. You may begin.

If there are identical symbols, put an "x" in the first box; if insects have six legs, underline the word "ant;" circle the star that has a white circle inside. You may begin.

Underline the multiple of seven; cross out the vowels in the predator; if there are more than three exclamation marks put a circle in the empty box; draw a box around the rectangle. You may begin.

Circle the multiple of seven; cross the vowels in something sweet; join the bottom point of the first triangle to the top point of the second; if both words have an "r" check the empty box. You may begin.

Part One...

...Concentration! – Teacher Copy ⬅||||

Concentration! – 4 ⬅||||

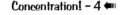

1.

2.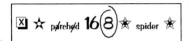

3.

4.

5.

Concentration! – 5 ⬅||||

1.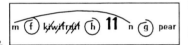

2.

3.

4.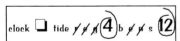

5. clock ☐ tide ~~r e d~~ ④ b ~~r e~~ s ⑫

Circle the numbers which can run consecutively; if any two numbers add to eighteen, check the third circle; if there is a letter that comes before "l" in the alphabet put an "x" in the first circle. You may begin.

If any numbers multiplied together make one of the other numbers, cross out the "t"s in "little"; if there is something mice like to eat, put an "x" in the second box. You may begin.

If there are identical symbols, put an "x" in the first box; circle the number that is half of another number; cross the vowels in the word that is opposite to "soaked." You may begin.

Circle any pairs of symbols; if birds give milk, circle the word milk; cross out the vowels in the citrus fruit; if there are two check marks, underline them both. You may begin.

Circle the star that has six points; underline the word that is something you can drink; cross out the multiple of seven; write the number of "b"s in the word "bubble" in the white star.   You may begin.

Cross any numbers that are multiples of three; underline anything that can be paddled with oars, check the empty box; draw a circle above two numbers that add up to forty-two. You may begin.

Circle the three letters that are consecutive in the alphabet; cross out the vowels in the fruit with green flesh; if there is a prime number, join the letter "m" to the letter "n." You may begin.

If there are identical symbols, join each to its partner with a curved line; circle the number which is double one of the other numbers; put a box around the smallest prime number. You may begin.

If any of the numbers can be divided equally by four, circle them; draw boxes around the three letters that are consecutive in the alphabet; if birds have beaks, underline the word "egg." You may begin.

Cross out the five letters that spell a color; circle the number to do with noon; if the first word has the same number of consonants that match one number, circle that number. You may begin.

Listen carefully to your teacher.

1. □ 11 □ 3 8 2 4

2. ○ l ☆ m p n

3. ○ ● ▲ ★ ☆ ☆

4. fluffy solid 19 14 machine 203

5. 77 23 r 44 p 99 q t

Concentration! – 1

Listen carefully to your teacher.

1. □ 11 □ 3 8 2 4

2. ○ l ☆ m p n

3. ○ ● ▲ ★ ☆ ☆

4. fluffy solid 19 14 machine 203

5. 77 23 r 44 p 99 q t

Listen carefully to your teacher.

1. ❄ ❄ float **19** **15** ❄ plug

2. **127 204** pear carrot **190** yacht

3. ★ ✦ ★

4. **4 7** heart circle **14 105** ○

5. elephant palm **19** ☛ **27 36** ☎ ✡

Concentration! – 2 ⬇

Listen carefully to your teacher.

1. ❄ ❄ float **19** **15** ❄ plug

2. **127 204** pear carrot **190** yacht

3. ★ ✦ ★

4. **4 7** heart circle **14 105** ○

5. elephant palm **19** ☛ **27 36** ☎ ✡

Concentration! – 3

Listen carefully to your teacher.

1. ★ ✡ **36** light **18** ◆ squirrel ★

2. telephone general **21** ☆ ▢ ☎ **19**

3. ▢ ✪ ☆ ☆ ant ✭ dolphin

4. **16** ! rabbit ! weasel **21** ! ! ▢ !

5. ▼ **23** dessert ▲ **63** scholar ▢

Concentration! – 3

Listen carefully to your teacher.

1. ★ ✡ **36** light **18** ◆ squirrel ★

2. telephone general **21** ☆ ▢ ☎ **19**

3. ▢ ✪ ☆ ☆ ant ✭ dolphin

4. **16** ! rabbit ! weasel **21** ! ! ▢ !

5. ▼ **23** dessert ▲ **63** scholar ▢

Concentration! – 4 ◀▥

Listen carefully to your teacher.

1. 7 ◯ 9 11 ◯ 8 21 m ◯

2. little cheese 27 ☐ 3 ◯ 8 9

3. ☐ ☆ parched 16 8 ☆ spider ✦

4. ✔ ☆ ✦ ✪ ✦ milk lemon

5. water ✂ ✦ ☆ bubble ✡ 49 15

Concentration! – 4 ◀▥

Listen carefully to your teacher.

1. 7 ◯ 9 11 ◯ 8 21 m ◯

2. little cheese 27 ☐ 3 ◯ 8 9

3. ☐ ☆ parched 16 8 ☆ spider ✦

4. ✔ ☆ ✦ ✪ ✦ milk lemon

5. water ✂ ✦ ☆ bubble ✡ 49 15

Listen carefully to your teacher.

1. 33 14 canoe ☐ liner 21 9 15

2. m f kiwifruit h 11 n g pear

3. ☆ ★ 48 ☆ 7 ★ 24 ☆ ★

4. egg w goat v p 128 q u mouse 45

5. clock ☐ tide r e g 4 b e n s 12

Concentration! – 5

Listen carefully to your teacher.

1. 33 14 canoe ☐ liner 21 9 15

2. m f kiwifruit h 11 n g pear

3. ☆ ★ 48 ☆ 7 ★ 24 ☆ ★

4. egg w goat v p 128 q u mouse 45

5. clock ☐ tide r e g 4 b e n s 12

Concentration!...

_____'s Scoring Sheet ◀▥

Activity	Score
Concentration! One	5
Concentration! Two	5
Concentration! Three	5
Concentration! Four	5
Concentration! Five	5

Concentration!...

_____'s Scoring Sheet ◀▥

Activity	Score
Concentration! One	5
Concentration! Two	5
Concentration! Three	5
Concentration! Four	5
Concentration! Five	5

Concentration!...

_____'s Scoring Sheet ◀▥

Activity	Score
Concentration! One	5
Concentration! Two	5
Concentration! Three	5
Concentration! Four	5
Concentration! Five	5

Part Two

...Item Missing ◀||||

In this section, students are required to listen carefully to two lists of items read by the teacher. They then write the missing item from the second list.

The *Item Missing* activities gradually become more complex. Therefore, it is suggested that you work through the sets of activities in the order they are presented. The activities are designed to develop listening and memory skills.

Instructions

▶ Discuss the fact that exercising or training the mind is similar to training a muscle... success will not be instantaneous, it takes regular practice.

▶ Use one set of *Item Missing* activities per session. Read both the initial list and the set in brackets, which has one item missing. Read them aloud to the students, slowly, deliberately and clearly, without stressing any particular item. The missing item in each list is in bold type.

▶ Once you have finished giving each list of items, the students then write the missing item on the scoring sheet on page 32. Give your students time to ponder.

Scoring

▶ Read the complete set again and supply the answer. Record scores on the scoring sheet on page 32.

▶ Tell your students that you expect them to be honest—they will only be cheating themselves if, for instance, they score their work incorrectly.

▶ By filling out their scoring sheets students will be able to monitor their progress, hopefully seeing the improvements they are making when they total their scores each month, assuming you are doing one set each week.

▶ If improvements are not being made, go back a level and give further practice until the student is ready to move on to a more advanced level.

▶ NOTE: The scoring sheets are designed so students can monitor their own individual progress—they are not designed to compare scores with anyone else. Please avoid asking the students to call their scores aloud in front of the class unless the students say they are quite comfortable with this. You may collect totals individually instead.

Item Missing ⬅️|||

Refer back to instructions for important details on administering and scoring. Use one set per session. Read the lists of items in each set to the students slowly and clearly without stressing any particular item.

5 Items – Set One ⬅️|||

1. comb, ribbon, **shine**, hair, shampoo
   (ribbon, comb, hair, shampoo)
2. tree, **green**, bird, nest, eggs
   (eggs, bird, tree, nest)
3. book, page, sentence, **phrase**, word
   (sentence, word, page, book)
4. **scissors**, ruler, eraser, paper clip, pen
   (pen, ruler, paper clip, eraser)

5 Items – Set Two ⬅️|||

1. dog, stick, tail, **chase**, tongue
   (tongue, dog, stick, tail)
2. **carols**, tree, star, baby, angel
   (baby, tree, star, angel)
3. book, **pages**, sea, smuggler, moon
   (book, smuggler, sea, moon)
4. sausage, barbecue, bread, **butter**, sauce
   (sauce, barbecue, sausage, bread)

5 Items – Set Three ⬅️|||

1. rainbow, red, green, **blue**, yellow
   (yellow, rainbow, red, green)
2. car, **gas**, trip, suitcase, apples
   (suitcase, trip, apples, car)
3. police, siren, **flashing**, ticket, speeding
   (ticket, speeding, police, siren)
4. phone, **book**, number, operator, dial
   (number, phone, operator, dial)

5 Items – Set Four ⬅️|||

1. sheep, pasture, shepherd, dog, **lamb**
   (dog, pasture, sheep, shepherd)
2. storm, **creaking**, hurricane, boat, waves
   (boat, storm, waves, hurricane)
3. sand, pail, **spade**, castle, shell
   (castle, shell, pail, sand)
4. cherry, icing, candle, **smile**, wish
   (icing, candle, cherry, wish)

5 Items – Set Five ⬅️|||

1. island, continent, **river**, lake, ocean
   (lake, continent, island, ocean)
2. **finger**, skin, nail, hair, tooth
   (nail, skin, tooth, hair)
3. bee, fly, mosquito, **wasp**, ant
   (ant, fly, mosquito, bee)
4. fence, **gate**, garage, tractor, latch
   (tractor, latch, garage, fence)

5 Items – Set Six ⬅️|||

1. tired, sleepy, awake, alert, **dreamy**
   (alert, awake, tired, sleepy)
2. box, **gift**, bow, tape, scissors
   (bow, tape, box, scissors)
3. battery, engine, **wheel**, seat, exhaust
   (seat, exhaust, engine, battery)
4. **laugh**, cry, scream, yawn, surprise
   (scream, cry, yawn, surprise)

5 Items – Set Seven ⬅️|||

1. apples, **bananas**, oranges, pears, grapes
   (oranges, grapes, apples, pears)
2. tie, **knot**, loop, twist, string
   (string, twist, tie, loop)
3. plan, map, chart, **poster**, board
   (board, chart, plan, map)
4. repair, fix, **break**, destroy, renovate
   (destroy, fix, renovate, repair)

5 Items – Set Eight ⬅️|||

1. cup, plate, bowl, **saucer**, pot
   (plate, pot, bowl, cup)
2. plant, pot, soil, water, **fertilizer**
   (pot, soil, plant, water)
3. wind, rain, snow, **sleet**, sun
   (sun, snow, rain, wind)
4. money, **bank**, purse, pocket, budget
   (pocket, budget, purse, money)

Item Missing ⬅||||

Refer back to instructions for important details on administering and scoring.
Use one set per session. Read the lists of items in each set to the students slowly and clearly without stressing any particular item.

6 Items – Set One ⬅||||

1. **roof**, windows, hair, apple, bird, pie
   (apple, bird, windows, pie, hair)
2. nail, hammer, hat, **wool**, ribbon, dog
   (hat, nail, ribbon, hammer, dog)
3. plane, truck, **air**, paper, metal, nail
   (paper, nail, metal, truck, plane)
4. ink, pen, **girl**, brush, truck, tree
   (pen, truck, tree, ink, brush)

6 Items – Set Two ⬅||||

1. water, fountain, juice, spray, **cream**, wet
   (juice, water, fountain, wet, spray)
2. sky, **blue**, hot, leaves, shade, white
   (white, leaves, hot, sky, shade)
3. lion, scream, ear, **yellow**, mane, eye
   (scream, eye, ear, mane, lion)
4. **whisker**, fur, cat, silky, twitch, claw
   (cat, twitch, fur, claw, silky)

6 Items – Set Three ⬅||||

1. **ruler**, pencil, test, try, hard, fly
   (test, hard, try, pencil, fly)
2. heat, **oven**, cake, cherry, nuts, fruit
   (cake, fruit, nuts, cherry, heat)
3. paint, water, **sketch**, artist, brush, draw
   (brush, draw, artist, water, paint)
4. lion, dog, mane, **fur**, bark, pride
   (lion, pride, mane, dog, bark)

6 Items – Set Four ⬅||||

1. mouse, hole, cheese, **trap**, cat, eyes
   (cheese, hole, mouse, cat, eyes)
2. velvet, **fabric**, silk, dress, fairy, ball
   (ball, fairy, velvet, dress, silk)
3. road, **truck**, sign, bridge, boy, bike
   (road, bike, boy, bridge, sign)
4. **milk**, white, cream, froth, cow, brown
   (brown, white, froth, cream, cow)

6 Items – Set Five ⬅||||

1. mouth, food, brush, teeth, stain, **gleam**
   (teeth, brush, mouth, food, stain)
2. river, bank, rat, toad, **boat**, ducks
   (rat, river, ducks, bank, toad)
3. box, gift, bow, **red**, teddy, golden
   (golden, teddy, bow, gift, box)
4. bush, house, ginger, witch, candy, **eaves**
   (bush, candy, witch, ginger, house)

6 Items – Set Six ⬅||||

1. **clock**, chime, hour, minute, hand, alarm
   (hour, chime, minute, alarm, hand)
2. candy, ice, sugar, candle, **match**, girl
   (ice, candy, candle, sugar, girl)
3. tiger, **snake**, giraffe, zoo, train, parrot
   (zoo, parrot, train, tiger, giraffe)
4. school, lunch, play, **book**, dog, swim
   (dog, swim, lunch, school, play)

6 Items – Set Seven ⬅||||

1. **vacation**, sand, beach, pines, picnic, tent
   (pines, sand, beach, tent, picnic)
2. fence, electric, deer, fawn, **buck**, horn
   (electric, deer, fence, horn, fawn)
3. moon, earth, **planet**, galaxy, eclipse, comet
   (comet, earth, eclipse, galaxy, moon)
4. mushroom, ring, pixie, dance, wizard, **spell**
   (wizard, pixie, mushroom, dance, ring)

6 Items – Set Eight ⬅||||

1. pirate, rigger, sail, haul, **barnacle**, salt
   (salt, pirate, rigger, sail, haul)
2. sea, foam, mermaid, ship, sailor, **siren**
   (ship, sailor, mermaid, sea, foam)
3. parade, float, band, marching, **pipes**, baby
   (baby, parade, band, marching, float)
4. apple, **red**, skin, tree, picker, ladder
   (tree, picker, ladder, apple, skin)

Item Missing...

_____'s Scoring Sheet ⬅️||||

➡ **5 Items – Set _____**

1. _____   2. _____   3. _____

4. _____   Total   _____

➡ **5 Items – Set _____**

1. _____   2. _____   3. _____

4. _____   Total   _____

➡ **5 Items – Set _____**

1. _____   2. _____   3. _____

4. _____   Total   _____

➡ **5 Items – Set _____**

1. _____   2. _____   3. _____

4. _____   Total   _____

Item Missing...

_____'s Scoring Sheet ⬅️||||

➡ **6 Items – Set _____**

1. _____   2. _____   3. _____

4. _____   Total   _____

➡ **6 Items – Set _____**

1. _____   2. _____   3. _____

4. _____   Total   _____

➡ **6 Items – Set _____**

1. _____   2. _____   3. _____

4. _____   Total   _____

➡ **6 Items – Set _____**

1. _____   2. _____   3. _____

4. _____   Total   _____

Part Three...

In this section, students are required to listen to a group of digits read by the teacher. They write the same sequence of digits from memory.

Instructions

➠ Discuss the fact that exercising or training the mind is somewhat similar to training a muscle... success will not be instantaneous, it takes regular practice.

➠ Use one set of *Digits Forwards* activities per session. Read one group of digits at a time aloud to the students, slowly and clearly, without stressing any particular digit.

➠ Once you have finished reading each group of digits, the students then write the same sequence of digits from memory on their scoring sheet. Stress that students are to refrain from writing until you have finished reading the group aloud. Give the students time to ponder. Repeat with each group of digits until the set is complete.

➠ A "challenge" from the next level is enjoyed by most students and one is provided for each set.

Scoring

➠ Read each group of digits in the set for students to check their answers. Use the scoring sheet on page 36 to record individual scores. The "challenge" is not recorded in the total on the scoring sheet—this is purely to help develop self-confidence.

➠ Tell your students that you expect them to be honest with themselves—they will be cheating only themselves if they score their work incorrectly, or begin to write the number before being told.

➠ By filling out their scoring sheets students will be able to monitor their progress and hopefully see the improvements they are making when they total their scores each month, assuming you are doing these each week.

➠ If improvements are not being made, go back a level and give further practice until the student is ready to move on to a more advanced level.

➠ NOTE: The scoring sheet on page 36 is designed so students can monitor their own individual progress—they are not designed to compare scores with anyone else. Please avoid asking the students to call their scores aloud in front of the class, unless the students say they are quite comfortable with this. You may collect totals individually instead.

Refer back to instructions for important details on administering and scoring.
Use one set per session. Read the groups of digits in each set to the students slowly and clearly without stressing any particular item.

7 Digits – Set One ◀llll

8957157	4879021	6590578
7803595	5783026	9598105

Challenge: 30579857

7 Digits – Set Two ◀llll

2028579	5971534	3135879
5490312	8947831	4968201

Challenge: 98570352

7 Digits – Set Three ◀llll

2505987	3597802	4874360
1297605	2079380	4489105

Challenge: 42187902

7 Digits – Set Four ◀llll

7302958	4187469	2363289
1018599	6543213	8241645

Challenge: 87954875

7 Digits – Set Five ◀llll

1959174	6586370	7982063
1505456	4852923	3205405

Challenge: 78452892

7 Digits – Set Six ◀llll

2369556	0125069	6851879
5492520	7485824	6894103

Challenge: 18452933

7 Digits – Set Seven ◀llll

4659821	5638974	5369876
5471479	3210508	9984557

Challenge: 31206897

7 Digits – Set Eight ◀llll

9874568	5258714	6396876
3125490	0366857	1147801

Challenge: 18339560

7 Digits – Set Nine ◀llll

5589574	3215477	6968871
0210784	6259814	3791375

Challenge: 10089574

7 Digits – Set Ten ◀llll

8684218	9794561	3579825
0219587	3575893	6546589

Challenge: 64569003

7 Digits – Set Eleven ◀llll

4147852	6598201	3216548
2057892	1591587	3571584

Challenge: 18465975

7 Digits – Set Twelve ◀llll

7418596	3565985	4613528
0269830	2574108	6528879

Challenge: 64025877

Refer back to instructions for important details on administering and scoring.
Use one set per session. Read the groups of digits in each set to the students slowly and clearly without stressing any particular item.

8 Digits – Set One ⬅III

55987586	66548920	32587458
15021785	36025984	33202658

Challenge: 636598751

8 Digits – Set Two ⬅III

52857481	32159857	20125874
12015784	36259802	20157894

Challenge: 989574855

8 Digits – Set Three ⬅III

55698574	26057884	65265412
20154639	98798574	35714892

Challenge: 421065987

8 Digits – Set Four ⬅III

79546310	25817390	82937415
20135718	98564213	23467985

Challenge: 552986230

8 Digits – Set Five ⬅III

55986471	52587100	30269875
42187598	52741890	32015487

Challenge: 665985471

8 Digits – Set Six ⬅III

58471499	65987401	14078366
54180709	30268971	20214785

Challenge: 198464417

8 Digits – Set Seven ⬅III

85958262	32015647	32659871
20154795	35735985	35894155

Challenge: 306598741

8 Digits – Set Eight ⬅III

46137988	59847104	30659801
10248759	32659871	25401897

Challenge: 629896588

8 Digits – Set Nine ⬅III

59874784	32658481	36981745
32654817	20150879	30669874

Challenge: 646689722

8 Digits – Set Ten ⬅III

98965870	20154879	65924701
70809837	20504887	90359877

Challenge: 645468971

8 Digits – Set Eleven ⬅III

71938375	82398233	46791477
82936871	61918172	37958417

Challenge: 392875105

8 Digits – Set Twelve ⬅III

89574158	98685920	30245874
59080741	36929186	11248793

Challenge: 546689321

Digits Forwards...

_____'s Scoring Sheet ⬅|||

➡ **7 Digits – Set** _____

_____ _____ _____ _____ _____

_____ Challenge _____   Total _____

➡ **7 Digits – Set** _____

_____ _____ _____ _____ _____

_____ Challenge _____   Total _____

➡ **7 Digits – Set** _____

_____ _____ _____ _____ _____

_____ Challenge _____   Total _____

➡ **7 Digits – Set** _____

_____ _____ _____ _____ _____

_____ Challenge _____   Total _____

Digits Forwards...

_____'s Scoring Sheet ⬅|||

➡ **8 Digits – Set** _____

_____ _____ _____ _____ _____

_____ Challenge _____   Total _____

➡ **8 Digits – Set** _____

_____ _____ _____ _____ _____

_____ Challenge _____   Total _____

➡ **8 Digits – Set** _____

_____ _____ _____ _____ _____

_____ Challenge _____   Total _____

➡ **8 Digits – Set** _____

_____ _____ _____ _____ _____

_____ Challenge _____   Total _____

Part Four...

In this section, students are required to listen to a group of digits read by the teacher. They write the same sequence of digits from memory in reverse order.

Instructions

▥➡ Use one set of *Digits Backwards* activities per session. Read one group of digits at a time aloud to the students slowly and clearly, without stressing any particular digit.

▥➡ Once you have finished reading each group of digits, the students then write the same sequence of digits from memory on their scoring sheet in reverse order. Stress that the students are to refrain from writing until you have finished reading the group aloud.

▥➡ Students should not write the digits down from right to left on their page, or write them from left to right and then rewrite them reversed; but should hold the sequence in their memory and turn it around. For example, if the sequence given is 456789, they should remember it, turn it around and write 987654.

▥➡ It should be stressed to the students that they are training their minds, in essence, to memorize and manipulate items. If they don't hold the sequence in their memory and turn it around before wriitng it down, they are not training themselves for subsequent sets. Honesty here sets them up for more difficult future sets. Honesty is the best policy.

▥➡ A "challenge" from the next level, is enjoyed by most students and one is provided for each set.

4123

Scoring

▥➡ Read each group of digits in reverse order for students to check their answers. Use the scoring sheet on page 40 to record individual scores. The "challenge" is not recorded in the total on the scoring sheet—this is purely to help develop self-confidence.

▥➡ By filling out their scoring sheets students will be able to monitor their progress and hopefully see the improvements they are making when they total their scores each month, assuming you are doing these each week.

▥➡ If improvements are not being made, go back a level and give further practice until the student is ready to move on to a more advanced level.

▥➡ NOTE: The scoring sheet on page 40 is designed so students can monitor their own individual progress—they are not designed to compare scores with anyone else. Please avoid asking the students to call their scores aloud in front of the class, unless the students say they are quite comfortable with this. You may collect totals individually instead.

Digits Backwards ⬅️IIII

Refer back to instructions for important details on administering and scoring.
Use one set per session. Read the groups of digits in each set to the students slowly and clearly without stressing any particular item.

6 Digits – Set One ⬅️IIII

498102	659858	215930
859214	369651	159570

Challenge: 5894101

6 Digits – Set Two ⬅️IIII

354219	135978	456280
024892	420159	463971

Challenge: 8972581

6 Digits – Set Three ⬅️IIII

352986	414895	152019
652930	258471	963652

Challenge: 1470232

6 Digits – Set Four ⬅️IIII

593024	452196	436975
810937	739105	546280

Challenge: 7591320

6 Digits – Set Five ⬅️IIII

782651	201398	420893
019837	402985	730255

Challenge: 4780232

6 Digits – Set Six ⬅️IIII

454830	416985	936587
864280	462989	252477

Challenge: 4369857

6 Digits – Set Seven ⬅️IIII

548862	489512	121587
465988	258741	357894

Challenge: 6549852

6 Digits – Set Eight ⬅️IIII

659865	458514	659805
154287	356901	100587

Challenge: 9865237

6 Digits – Set Nine ⬅️IIII

465259	245870	254074
202785	379899	252874

Challenge: 4312587

6 Digits – Set Ten ⬅️IIII

228579	653684	445782
250078	431856	464870

Challenge: 3210985

6 Digits – Set Eleven ⬅️IIII

987958	283917	718554
548701	306089	411875

Challenge: 6532985

6 Digits – Set Twelve ⬅️IIII

487589	894217	325407
201765	852785	257419

Challenge: 9872625

Refer back to instructions for important details on administering and scoring.
Use one set per session. Read the groups of digits in each set to the students slowly and clearly without stressing any particular item.

7 Digits – Set One ◀‖‖

9858475	1254879	3635985
4584932	1205708	2578910

Challenge: 31356874

7 Digits – Set Two ◀‖‖

5878146	3560280	2541789
2014755	6652014	1859765

Challenge: 98765845

7 Digits – Set Three ◀‖‖

4896525	9598702	3584952
2505813	3156487	0215048

Challenge: 13254974

7 Digits – Set Four ◀‖‖

5985877	3561028	8570154
1054239	5801512	6541050

Challenge: 75329857

7 Digits – Set Five ◀‖‖

6595714	1542080	2698657
3032587	4839751	2058741

Challenge: 47125988

7 Digits – Set Six ◀‖‖

5985687	2502598	4679135
5281739	5468972	5918473

Challenge: 43152987

7 Digits – Set Seven ◀‖‖

8957415	2560254	4620159
4612574	4596863	3568975

Challenge: 65689557

7 Digits – Set Eight ◀‖‖

9263598	1542510	1050598
7884014	8593115	7544710

Challenge: 98596001

7 Digits – Set Nine ◀‖‖

7984512	4857022	3625852
4875998	2124366	6814046

Challenge: 43126877

7 Digits – Set Ten ◀‖‖

3322154	5963511	4758210
4653289	1049036	6875770

Challenge: 32169857

7 Digits – Set Eleven ◀‖‖

5847124	3026890	4047855
7971478	0074589	6404580

Challenge: 98970144

7 Digits – Set Twelve ◀‖‖

4325987	1502487	3569805
1050697	4456282	8784581

Challenge: 65478237

Digits Backwards...

_____'s Scoring Sheet ◀||||

➠ **6 Digits – Set** _____

_____ _____ _____ _____ _____

_____ Challenge _____   Total _____

➠ **6 Digits – Set** _____

_____ _____ _____ _____ _____

_____ Challenge _____   Total _____

➠ **6 Digits – Set** _____

_____ _____ _____ _____ _____

_____ Challenge _____   Total _____

➠ **6 Digits – Set** _____

_____ _____ _____ _____ _____

_____ Challenge _____   Total _____

Digits Backwards...

_____'s Scoring Sheet ◀||||

➠ **7 Digits – Set** _____

_____ _____ _____ _____ _____

_____ Challenge _____   Total _____

➠ **7 Digits – Set** _____

_____ _____ _____ _____ _____

_____ Challenge _____   Total _____

➠ **7 Digits – Set** _____

_____ _____ _____ _____ _____

_____ Challenge _____   Total _____

➠ **7 Digits – Set** _____

_____ _____ _____ _____ _____

_____ Challenge _____   Total _____